Master KS2 Reading with CGP!

When it comes to reading in Year 5, practice makes perfect. That's why CGP have made this indispensable Question Book!

It's full of fascinating texts by a variety of authors — each with practice questions to check pupils' understanding and deepen their knowledge of techniques used by authors.

We've even included helpful answers at the back of the book.

What CGP is all about

Our sole aim here at CGP is to produce the highest quality books — carefully written, immaculately presented and dangerously close to being funny.

Then we work our socks off to get them out to you — at the cheapest possible prices.

Contents

Published by CGP

Anthologist: Christopher Edge
Questions written by Amanda MacNaughton
Consultant: Julie Docker
Reviewers: Sam Bensted, Juliette Green, Maxine Petrie
Editors: Melissa Gardner, Kelsey Hammond, Christopher Lindle, Sam Norman, Gabrielle Richardson, Rosa Roberts

With thanks to Izzy Bowen, Alison Griffin, Sophie Herring and Holly Robinson for the proofreading.
With thanks to Ana Pungartnik for the copyright research.

ISBN: 978 1 78908 358 3
Printed by Elanders Ltd, Newcastle upon Tyne.

About this Book

This book consists of nine stimulating texts for pupils to read, with two sets of questions for each text:

- Question Set 1 checks that pupils understand the text as a whole, with lots of retrieval questions.
- Question Set 2 gets pupils thinking more deeply, with more questions requiring inference.

Question Pages

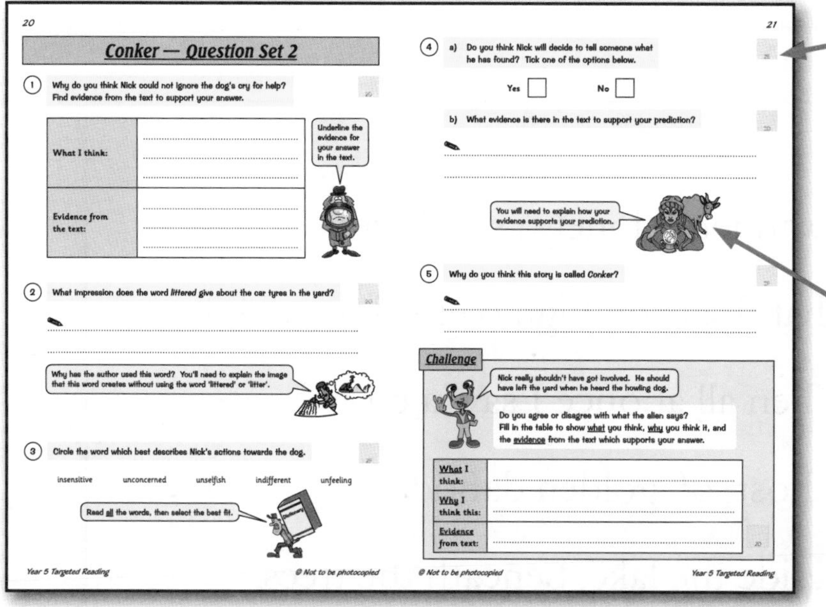
20

Conker — Question Set 2

1. Why do you think Nick could not ignore the dog's cry for help? Find evidence from the text to support your answer.

What I think:	
Evidence from the text:	

2. What impression does the word *littered* give about the car tyres in the yard?

3. Circle the word which best describes Nick's actions towards the dog.

insensitive unconcerned unselfish indifferent unfeeling

4. a) Do you think Nick will decide to tell someone what he has found? Tick one of the options below.

Yes ☐ No ☐

b) What evidence is there in the text to support your prediction?

5. Why do you think this story is called *Conker*?

Challenge

Do you agree or disagree with what the alien says?
Fill in the table to show what you think, why you think it, and the evidence from the text which supports your answer.

What I think:	
Why I think this:	
Evidence from text:	

The mark boxes give the national curriculum content area for the question:

2B

Pupils are given tips on how to tackle some questions.

The recurring characters familiarise pupils with different types of question:

Scanning the text

Finding evidence in the text

National Curriculum References

Here is a key to the national curriculum references for the different question types:

2A	give / explain the meaning of words in context
2B	retrieve and record information / identify key details from fiction and non-fiction
2C	summarise main ideas from more than one paragraph
2D	make inferences from the text / explain and justify inferences with evidence from the text
2E	predict what might happen from details stated and implied
2F	identify / explain how information / narrative content is related and contributes to meaning as a whole
2G	identify / explain how meaning is enhanced through choice of words and phrases
2H	make comparisons within the text

At the back of the book, you'll find a table where you can record the pupil's performance in the different content areas:

		National Curriculum Content Areas							
		2a Word Meaning	2b Retrieval	2c Summarising	2d Inference	2e Prediction	2f Text Meaning	2g Language	2h Comparison
Text 1: Daffodils	Set 1	Q4	Q1 Q2	Q6	Q5			Q3	
	Set 2	Q3		Q5	Q2b Ch		Q2a	Q1	Q4
Text 2: Winter Paralympics	Set 1		Q2 Q3 Q4	Q1			Q6		Q5
	Set 2	Q2	Q4		Q3 Ch			Q1 Q5	
Text 3: Conker	Set 1	Q6	Q1 Q2 Q3 Q4	Q5					
	Set 2				Q1 Q4b Ch	Q4a	Q3 Q5	Q2	

Daffodils

Start reading here. There might be important information in the introduction.

Poets can use figurative language such as similes to help the reader picture the images their words describe. Here, William Wordsworth uses similes and personification in this poem about daffodils.

I wandered lonely as a cloud
That floats on high o'er vales and hills,
When all at once I saw a crowd,
A host, of golden daffodils;
Beside the lake, beneath the trees,
Fluttering and dancing in the breeze.

Continuous as the stars that shine
And twinkle on the milky way,
They stretched in never-ending line
Along the margin of a bay:
Ten thousand saw I at a glance,
Tossing their heads in sprightly dance.

The waves beside them danced; but they
Out-did the sparkling waves in glee:
A poet could not but be gay,
In such a jocund company:
I gazed - and gazed - but little thought
What wealth the show to me had brought:

For oft, when on my couch I lie
In vacant or in pensive mood,
They flash upon that inward eye
Which is the bliss of solitude;
And then my heart with pleasure fills,
And dances with the daffodils.

William Wordsworth

Consider

Think of other things in nature e.g. old oak trees, a waterfall or the night sky. What similes and metaphors could you use to describe them? Could you personify them in some way?

Daffodils — Question Set 1

1 **What does the poet compare himself to? Tick one box.** 2B

a daffodil ☐ a cloud ☐

a crowd ☐ a lake ☐

2 **Draw lines to match the forms of nature to where they are found in the poem.** 2B

the cloud	next to the daffodils
the daffodils	on the Milky Way
the stars	above the hills
the waves	under the trees

When you have to match, do the ones you're sure of first.

3 **Find and copy two phrases from the poem which show personification being used to describe the daffodils.** 2G

1. ....

2. ....

Personification is when the writer gives human characteristics to something non-human.

4 **The poet describes the company of the daffodils as *jocund*. Which of the following words do you think is most similar in meaning to *jocund*?** 2A

Tick one box

miserable ☐

chaotic ☐

cheerful ☐

lonely ☐

When you have to identify the meaning of a word, read around that word in the text to get a feeling of the mood.

Dictionary

5 **How does the poet feel when he thinks back to his vision of the daffodils? Find some evidence in the poem to support your answer.** 2D

....

....

....

You have been asked to find evidence. This means you need to copy some words from the text which prove your answer.

6 **Number the summary of each verse in the poem so they are in the correct order.** 2C

The poet describes numerous rows of daffodils moving. ☐

The poet recalls the pleasing sight of the daffodils. ☐

The poet describes his first sighting of the daffodils. ☐

The poet compares the daffodils to the beauty of the water. ☐

You have to crack the four-digit code. First <u>label</u> the verses of the poem with key words from the summaries (e.g. 'numerous rows', 'pleasing sight'). <u>Number</u> these 1-4 in the text in the order of the verses, then <u>match</u> the summaries in the question to your numbered list.

Daffodils — Question Set 2

(1) **Read the phrases taken from the poem and decide which of them are similes.** 2G

	Simile
lonely as a cloud	☐
The waves beside them danced	☐
my heart... dances with the daffodils	☐
Continuous as the stars that shine	☐

(2) **a) Which of the words below best describes how the poet feels about the daffodils. Circle your answer.** 2F

impressed heartened relaxed cheerful

b) Use evidence from the poem to justify your answer in part a). 2D

....

....

....

....

(3) **Match the word on the left with the correct definition on the right.** 2A

host	narrow strip
margin	happiness
sprightly	group
pensive	energetic
bliss	thoughtful

Replace the word in the poem with the definition to see if it makes sense.

Dictionary

4 The poet compares the daffodils with the waves on the lake. Which do you think he is more impressed by and why?

2H

....

....

....

5 This poem is written in 4 stanzas (verses), each with 6 lines. Which one of the following structures represents the rhyme scheme used in each stanza?

2C

ABABAB ☐ AABBCC ☐ ABCABC ☐ ABABCC ☐

The following poem shows how rhyme schemes work:

How deep is the water?	A	The first rhyme is always 'A'.
How deep is the sea?	B	'Sea' doesn't rhyme with 'water', so it's given the next letter (B).
It's as wide as the chasm	C	'Chasm' doesn't rhyme with either 'water' or 'sea', so it's given the next letter (C).
Between you and me.	B	'Me' rhymes with 'sea', so it's given the letter of the second rhyme (B).

Challenge

I didn't know daffodils had heads and could dance — that's amazing! I'm off on my walk soon. I'll look out for some of these daffodils.

Can you explain why the poet has suggested the daffodils can dance and what he really means?

....

....

....

....

....

2D

Winter Paralympics

Newspapers report on sporting events. The following article is taken from *The Guardian* newspaper and is about the 2018 Winter Paralympics, which took place in Pyeonchang in South Korea.

Winter Paralympics: the best bits from the Pyeongchang Games

Records tumbled as South Korea hosted the biggest and most-watched edition of the Winter Paralympics to date.

by Martin Belam

The 12th Winter Paralympics have come to an end in Pyeongchang, South Korea. Here are a pick of the highlights from 10 days of action, featuring athletes from 49 countries.

Records broken all around

It's traditional for every Games to be hailed as "the best ever" in the celebratory speeches at the closing ceremony, but Pyeongchang truly did set a number of new records for the Winter Paralympics. The number of tickets sold exceeded those sold at Sochi, and were the most ever, with the audience for the Winter Paralympics tripling since the 2006 Turin edition.

Brian McKeever set a record by wining his 13th Paralympic gold in his fifth appearance at the Games. He's now the most decorated Canadian Paralympian of all time, and the most successful Paralympian cross-country skier of all-time. Henrieta Farkasova, competing in the visually impaired alpine skiing, was the most decorated athlete — with four golds and a silver to take home to Slovakia.

Country debuts and first gold medals

As well as a larger audience, the Pyeongchang Games featured more athletes taking part from more countries than ever before. A record 20 different nations earned at least one gold medal, and 26 out of the 49 countries taking part won at least one medal, a higher percentage than at any Paralympics since Lillehammer in 1994.

Georgia, North Korea and Tajikistan all took part in the Winter Paralympics for the first time. China, who host the next edition, won gold at the Games for the very first time, as did Kazakhstan.

Records set for Paralympics GB

The British Paralympic team will return home on Monday boasting of a successful Games, having hit their medal target of between six and 12 medals. The seven medals won was one more than in Sochi.

All of the medals were down to the work of two Paralympians and their guides. Menna Fitzpatrick and Millie Knight won medals across a range of alpine skiing disciplines, with Fitzpatrick and her guide Jen Kehoe winning Britain's gold medal on the final morning of the Games.

Fitzpatrick said she wanted to celebrate with a "proper cup of English tea". By taking four medals in total, the 19 year old became the most decorated British Winter Paralympian of all-time.

Discuss

Imagine you were asked to plan a newspaper article about your school's sports day. Think of a headline and subheadings you could use. Who would you ask for a quote? Discuss your ideas with a partner.

Winter Paralympics — Question Set 1

1. **Which of these statements best summarises the purpose of the newspaper article?** 2C

Tick one box

To inform people of the decline in viewers of the Paralympics.	☐
To share the success of the South Korea Winter Paralympics.	☐
To encourage people to vote to have the next Paralympics back in South Korea.	☐
To celebrate the hundreds of medals won by Great Britain in the 2018 Winter Paralympics.	☐

2. **What record has the Paralympian Brian McKeever set for his country?** 2B

....

....

3. **Draw lines to match the country with the correct information.** 2B

China	took part in the 2018 Winter Paralympics for the first time
Slovakia	has produced the most successful cross-country Paralympian of all time
South Korea	held the most watched Winter Paralympics to date
Canada	will welcome home a Paralympian who has won 4 golds and 1 silver
Tajikistan	will host the Winter Paralympics next time

4 **Names of places have been matched with the year the Paralympics were or will be held there. Identify which are true and which are false.** 2B

	True	False
1994 China	☐	☐
2006 Turin	☐	☐
2018 South Korea	☐	☐
2022 Lillehammer	☐	☐

Scan the text for the place names and then read around that part of the text.

5 **List three ways in which the Pyeongchang Games were different from previous years.** 2H

Use the subheadings to help navigate around the newspaper report.

1. ....

2. ....

3. ....

6 **Each of these extracts is an example of a newspaper article feature. Match the extract with the correct feature.** 2F

Extract	Feature
'...and 26 out of the 49 countries taking part won at least one medal.'	headline
'Country debuts and first gold medals'	facts and figures
'Winter Paralympics: the best bits from the Pyeongchang Games'	quote
'Fitzpatrick said she wanted to celebrate with a "proper cup of English tea".'	subheading

When you have to match answers, do the ones you're most sure of first.

Winter Paralympics — Question Set 2

1 **What do the words *pick of the highlights* suggest about these games?** 2G

....

....

2 **Which of the following words would best replace the word *decorated* in the context of this article?** 2A

Tick one box

lovely ☐

successful ☐

old ☐

lucky ☐

This word appears several times in the text. Find an instance of the word and try to work out the meaning. Then find another instance of the word, and check whether your answer still makes sense.

3 **What do you think Menna Fitzpatrick means when she says she wants to celebrate with a *<u>proper</u> cup of English tea*?** 2D

....

....

....

For this question you have to get into the mind of the person speaking. Look at the underlined word in the quote — this may give you clue.

4 **Number these athletes/countries from 1-4 according to the number of medals they won at the Winter Paralympics. Put '1' next to the athlete/country that won the most.**

2B

Henrieta Farkasova ☐

Team GB ☐

Menna Fitzpatrick ☐

Millie Knight ☐

You might have to do a bit of maths for this question. Read the question carefully to make sure you number them in the right way.

5 **Find three words or phrases in the text which show that the British Paralympians did well at these games.**

2G

1. ....

2. ....

3. ....

Challenge

This newspaper article is packed with evidence that the Winter Paralympics have been held before but this tortoise can't find any of it. Help him to find the evidence by writing down four phrases.

1. ....

2. ....

3. ....

4. ....

2D

Conker

Remember to read the introduction. It might contain important information.

Michael Morpurgo has written over a hundred books for children and many of his stories feature animals. The following extract is taken from the short story *Conker* which is about a boy called Nick whose pet dog, Old Station, has been put down. Here, Nick is looking for some conkers and spots some just inside a scrapyard called Cotter's Yard.

There was no sign of life in Cotter's Yard. No one would be there on a Sunday afternoon. No one would mind if he went in just to pick up conkers. There was nothing wrong with that, he thought.

He climbed quickly. At the top he swung his legs over and dropped down easily on the other side. He found the cluster of three small conkers and broke them open. Each one was shining brown and perfect, and just the right size. He stuffed them into his pocket and was just about to climb out again when he heard from somewhere behind him in Cotter's Yard, the distant howling of a dog. His first thought was to scramble up over the fence and escape, but then the howling stopped and the dog began to whine and whimper and yelp. It was a cry for help which Nick could not ignore.

Cotter's Yard was a maze of twisted rusting wrecks. The muddy tracks through it were littered with car tyres. Great piles of cars towered all about him now as he picked his way round the potholes. And all the while the pitiful howling echoed louder around him. He was getting closer.

He found the guard dog sitting by a hut in the centre of the yard. He was chained by the neck to a metal stake, and he was shivering so much that his teeth were rattling. The chain was twisted over his back and wrapped around his back legs so that he could not move.

Doesn't look ferocious, Nick thought, *but you never know*. And he walked slowly around the guard dog at a safe distance.

And then Nick noticed the dog's face. It was as if Old Station had come back from the grave and was looking up at him. He had the same gentle brown eyes, the same way of holding his head on one side when he was thinking. *Old Station liked jelly babies*, Nick thought. *Perhaps this one will.* One by one the dog took them gently out of Nick's hand, chewed them, swallowed them and then waited for the next one.

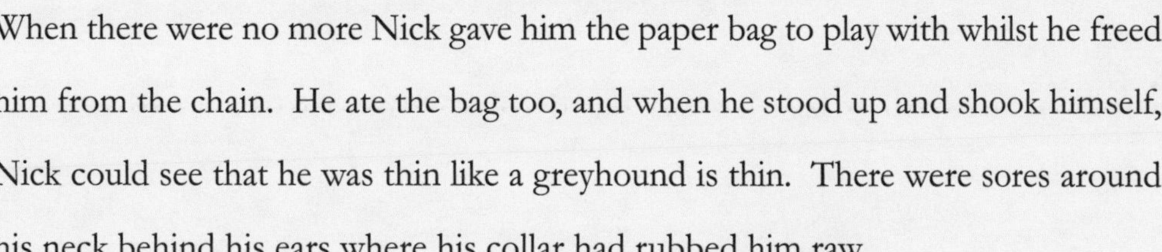

When there were no more Nick gave him the paper bag to play with whilst he freed him from the chain. He ate the bag too, and when he stood up and shook himself, Nick could see that he was thin like a greyhound is thin. There were sores around his neck behind his ears where his collar had rubbed him raw.

Nick sat down beside him, took off his duffel coat and rubbed him and rubbed him until his teeth stopped chattering. He didn't like to leave him, but it was getting dark.

"Don't worry," Nick said, walking away. The dog followed him to the end of his chain. "I'll be back," he said. "I promise I will."

An extract from *Conker* by Michael Morpurgo.

Discuss

**How does the end of this extract make you feel?
If you could write the following part of the story what would you want to happen? Discuss with a partner.**

Conker — Question Set 1

① **Why did Nick go into Cotter's Yard?** 2B

....

② **Write down three things that can be found in Cotter's Yard.** 2B

1. ....

2. ....

3. ....

③ **What is stopping the dog from escaping from Cotter's Yard?** 2B

Tick all that apply

He is fastened to a post by a chain. ☐

He is trapped in a hut in the middle of the yard. ☐

A chain is wrapped around his front legs. ☐

A chain is wrapped around his hind legs. ☐

If it says 'Tick all that apply', you're probably looking for more than one answer.

The words used in the statements might not be exactly the same as those used in the text. You will need to read the complete sentences carefully to see if the meaning is the same.

4 **Give three ways in which the dog that Nick discovers in Cotter's Yard is like Old Station.** 2B

1. ....

2. ....

3. ....

5 **Number these events in the order they happened in the extract.** 2C

Nick rubbed the dog until he was warmer. ☐

The dog ate the jelly babies one by one. ☐

Nick heard the noise of a dog in pain. ☐

The dog was untangled from the chain. ☐

Nick climbed into the yard. ☐

Find and underline each of the events in the story. Then number the events in the text in the order they appear. Finally, match the events in the question to the numbered events in the text.

6 ***Doesn't look ferocious, Nick thought, but you never know.*** **What does the phrase *but you never know* mean in this instance?** 2A

....

....

Think about how this phrase is used in everyday life.

Dictionary

Conker — Question Set 2

1 **Why do you think Nick could not ignore the dog's cry for help? Find evidence from the text to support your answer.** 2D

What I think:	....
Evidence from the text:	....

Underline the evidence for your answer in the text.

2 **What impression does the word *littered* give about the car tyres in the yard?** 2G

....

....

Why has the author used this word? You'll need to explain the image that this word creates without using the word 'littered' or 'litter'.

3 **Circle the word which best describes Nick's actions towards the dog.** 2F

insensitive   unconcerned   unselfish   indifferent   unfeeling

Read <u>all</u> the words, then select the best fit.

Dictionary

4 a) Do you think Nick will decide to tell someone what he has found? Tick one of the options below. 2E

Yes ☐ No ☐

b) What evidence is there in the text to support your prediction? 2D

....

....

You will need to explain how your evidence supports your prediction.

5 Why do you think this story is called *Conker*? 2F

....

....

Challenge

Nick really shouldn't have got involved. He should have left the yard when he heard the howling dog.

Do you agree or disagree with what the alien says?
Fill in the table to show what you think, why you think it, and the evidence from the text which supports your answer.

What I think:	....
Why I think this:	....
Evidence from text:	....

2D

The Coming of Raven

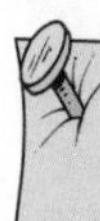

Myths are traditional stories told by different cultures that try to explain why the world is the way it is. The following text is a retelling of a myth told by the Inuit people, who live in the Arctic regions of Canada, Greenland and Alaska. In this story, Raven has created the Earth, the Sun and the Inuit people, telling them how to hunt but making them promise that they will not kill more animals than they need to live.

In time, there were more men and women, and they produced children. They chopped down forests to make houses; they made thread out of the sinews of animals and needles from their bones. They killed more and more animals. The Earth, sea and sky were plundered as the people became greedy, always wanting more. Earth cried out in pain and Raven heard its cry.

"Do you not remember your promise, oh Inuit people," cawed Raven angrily, "only to take what you need?"

But by this time the Inuit people no longer listened to Raven. They had forgotten their promise, and did not care about anything except their own desires. So Raven took a bag made from caribou skin. He soared towards the sun, grabbed it, stuffed it into the bag and flew back to Skyland. The world was plunged into darkness.

"Oh, oh, oh!" howled the Inuit. "We can't see, we can't keep warm, please give us back the sun."

So every now and then, Raven took pity on the people and uncovered the sun for a few days to allow them to hunt.

Now Raven thought he should have a companion. So he took Snow Goose to be his wife, and they had a son called Raven Boy. Sometimes, Raven showed his son the caribou skin bag and the sun inside it. Raven Boy became fascinated by the fiery rock.

One day, while his father was sleeping, Raven Boy crept up to the bag, determined to open it and see the sun. But Raven woke up. Fearful of his father's anger, Raven Boy fled with the bag to the other side of the universe and hid.

Below on Earth, without any sunshine at all, everything began to die. "Please save us, O Raven, creator of the universe. Give us back the sun!" implored the Inuit.

Raven took pity and went to look for his son. He cawed, "Raven Boy! Don't hide. Bring back the sun, or the world I created will die!"

Raven Boy heard his father's plea. He ripped open the bag and flung the sun spinning across the sky.

But so that the Inuits would remember the terror of darkness, Raven created night and day, winter and summer. And the Inuit never forgot their promise again. For ever after they respected all animals, and honoured Raven.

An extract from *The Coming of Raven* by Jamila Gavin.

Discuss

Do you think humans nowadays treat nature and the Earth correctly? Do they take too much from the Earth? Are humans selfish when it comes to using the Earth and its resources?

The Coming of Raven — Question Set 1

1 **Decide whether these statements are true or false.** 2B

	True	False
The Inuits are from the Arctic regions of Canada, Greenland and Alaska.	☐	☐
The Earth and the Sun were created by the Inuit people.	☐	☐
Needles were made from the bones of animals.	☐	☐
Raven was always pleased with the actions of the Inuit people.	☐	☐

2 **Which word in the text shows how quickly the darkness fell upon the Inuit people?** 2A

When you scan the text for an answer, make sure you start from the top of the text.

....

3 **When Raven takes the Sun away, what three things can the Inuits no longer do?** 2B

1. ....

2. ....

3. ....

4 **Why did Raven Boy hide on the other side of the universe?** 2B

....

....

5 **In what order did the following events happen in the story? Write a number next to each event. The first one has been done for you.** 2C

Raven Boy fled to the other side of the universe.	
Raven took pity on the people for the first time.	
The Inuits became greedy.	1
Raven created day and night and summer and winter.	
Raven took pity on the people for the second time.	
Raven took the sun away.	

Here you have to find the 6-digit secret code. Remember you can always jot numbers down outside the boxes first, before writing in your final answers.

6 **Draw lines to match each word on the left with its definition on the right. One has been done for you.** 2A

sinews	robbed
plundered	friend
companion	begged
implored	respected
honoured	ligaments

(sinews is matched to ligaments.)

Do the ones you know for definite first. This will make it easier to work out the ones you're not so sure of.

Dictionary

The Coming of Raven — Question Set 2

1. **Look at the paragraph beginning *But by this time the Inuit people...* Why did Raven decide to plunge them into darkness?** 2B

....

....

....

2. **Myths are traditional stories that aren't literally true. Find three pieces of evidence from the text which prove this story cannot be true. The first one has been done for you.** 2G

1. Earth cried out in pain

2. ....

3. ....

3. **a) From reading the text, which one of the following phrases best describes how Raven Boy feels about his father?** 2D

Tick one box

He has no respect for him. ☐

He is afraid of him. ☐

He admires him. ☐

He thinks he is clever. ☐

Make sure you select an answer that you can support with evidence.

b) Why do you think this? 2D

....

....

....

4 **Which of the following best represents how the Inuit people change over time?** 2H

Tick one box

unhappy - respectful - disobedient	☐
unhappy - disobedient - respectful	☐
disobedient - unhappy - respectful	☐
disobedient - respectful - unhappy	☐

5 **Why do you think the author used the words *Earth cried out in pain*?** 2G

....

....

....

When you are asked to work out why certain words are used, you need to say what the words mean and explain what image is created or how they make the reader feel.

Challenge

Do you think Raven is good or bad at being in charge?
Or do you think he's somewhere in between?
Give reasons and evidence from the text to support your answer.

....

....

....

....

....

....

2D

Helicopters

Helicopters are a type of aircraft that uses rotating blades to fly. The first modern helicopter was invented in the 1930s, but the idea for helicopters had been around much longer. This text explains how helicopters fly and how they were invented.

How Do Helicopters Fly?

At first glance, a helicopter seems a rather improbable flying machine. Unlike a plane, it doesn't even have wings. Yet a helicopter can take off without a runway, it can hover, and it can fly forwards, backwards or sideways. So how does a helicopter get off the ground, let alone stay in the air?

The key mechanical features of a helicopter are its spinning sets of blades, called rotors. These rotors are powered by an engine. The blades are specially shaped, like wings, so that when the rotor spins, the air moves over the blades more quickly than it moves underneath them. This creates a force called lift, which makes the helicopter rise into the air. Helicopter blades have to spin incredibly quickly to generate lift — around 500 rotations per minute.

If it only had one rotor, the forces acting on the helicopter would cause it to spin, so helicopters also have a smaller tail rotor to balance these forces. The pilot steers the helicopter by tilting the blades to increase the amount of lift on that blade.

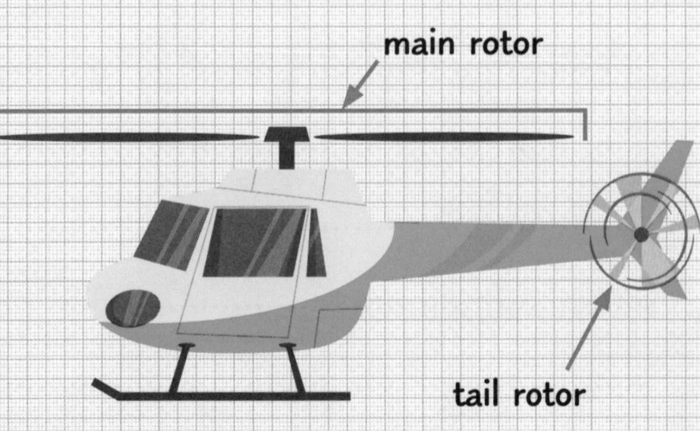

A Long History of Lift

The basic idea of using a rotor in a flying machine is nothing new. In the 1490s, Leonardo da Vinci famously drew a design for a spiral-shaped "airscrew". However, children in China were playing with "bamboo-copters" as long ago as 400 BC. Hundreds of years later, scientists and engineers in Europe were inspired by these bamboo blades.

They began experimenting with toy helicopters, but it wasn't until the invention of the internal combustion engine in the 1800s that engineers were able to spin rotors fast enough to lift a full-size helicopter into the air.

The world's first practical helicopter — a machine with both a main rotor and a tail rotor — wasn't unveiled until 1939. The VS-300 was designed by Igor Sikorsky. Its first flight lasted only a few seconds, but the design became the basis for the first mass-produced helicopters.

Today, helicopters are used for many purposes, including for travel, military transport, air ambulances and fighting forest fires. The world's biggest helicopter is the Halo, which can carry up to 56 tonnes (about the same weight as 10 African elephants) and has space for 80 passengers. In the future, helicopters may even be used in space. Engineers at NASA are developing a helicopter to explore Mars. Mars has a much thinner atmosphere than the Earth, which means that the rotors have to spin about ten times faster to create lift.

Written by Katharine Howell

Discuss

How might a Mars helicopter differ from an Earth helicopter? Discuss your ideas with a partner.

Helicopters — Question Set 1

(1) **Which word in the first paragraph suggests that helicopters don't look like they should be able to fly?** 2A

....

(2) **a) Label the diagram by writing the words from the box on the correct lines.** 2B

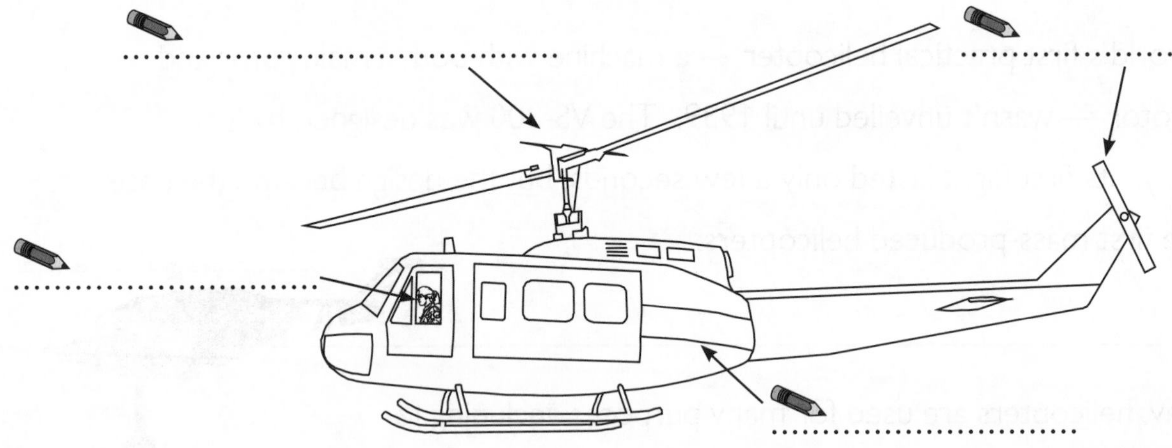

b) Draw lines to match the labelled parts (on the left) with their functions (on the right). 2B

main rotor	balances the forces acting on the helicopter
engine	steers the helicopter by tilting the blades
tail rotor	spins quickly to create lift
pilot	powers the rotors

3 **How much do the blades have to spin to generate lift?** 2B

....

This question is asking 'how much', so you're looking for an amount.

Who?
What?
Where?
When?
Why?

4 **Number the following statements about the history of the helicopter to put them in the order they happened. The last one has been done for you.** 2B

The internal combustion engine was invented. ☐

Leonardo da Vinci designed a spiral-shaped airscrew. ☐

The world's first helicopter took flight. ☐

Children in China played with bamboo-copters. ☐

Helicopters began to be used for air ambulances. 5

5 **What part did Igor Sikorsky play in the history of the helicopter? Tick your answer.** 2B

Tick one box

He designed the first spiral-shaped airscrew. ☐

He developed a helicopter that could fly to Mars. ☐

He designed the VS-300. ☐

He was the first pilot to fly in a helicopter. ☐

6 **Copy the opening words of the paragraph which explains the importance of having more that one set of blades.** 2C

....

Helicopters — Question Set 2

1 **Why does the first paragraph end with a question?** 2F

....

....

2 **Read these comparisons carefully, then use the text to help you decide if they are true or false. Tick your answers.** 2H

	True	False
It is easier for a helicopter to fly on Mars than on Earth.	☐	☐
The Halo helicopter is larger than the VS-300 helicopter.	☐	☐
The blades on a helicopter are motionless like the wings on a plane.	☐	☐

Don't get too 'tick-happy' with these True or False questions. Take your time, and find the part of the text which gives you the relevant information.

3 **Find and copy the phrase in the text which shows how important the "bamboo-copters" were in the invention of the helicopter.** 2G

....

In 'Find and copy' questions, always double-check that you haven't made any mistakes in copying the words from the text.

4 **Why do you think the author chose to give the information *about the same weight as 10 African elephants* in addition to the actual weight the Halo can carry?**

2G

How does this extra information help the reader?

....

....

5 **In the phrase *but the design became the basis for the first mass-produced helicopters*, what does *became the basis* mean?**

2A

....

....

Challenge

The first flight was only a few seconds. Igor Sikorsky didn't do very well with his design did he?

Tick a box to show whether you agree or disagree with the dog. Then complete the table to explain what you think of the first flight and why you think this.

Agree ☐ Disagree ☐

What you think about the first flight:	....
Why you think this:	....

2D

It's Today

Remember to read the introduction. It might contain important information.

This extract is from a story about Mira, a ten-year-old girl from a village in Mozambique, a country in southern Africa. Mira's brother has had to leave the village to study, but today he's returning for his coming-of-age ceremony...

"Mira! Mira! Wake up!"

It's so early that the sun hasn't risen yet, so I roll over and pretend to be asleep. Mama comes into the hut, reaches under the mosquito net and tickles my foot.

"OK, I'm coming," I mumble, clambering out of bed and trying not to wake my little sister Olga and niece Dinoka, who share the bed with me.

I stumble outside. Mama is sitting in the yard next to a big pile of sorghum, hitting it with a stick so that the grains break off the stems, dancing everywhere. My cousin Nissia arrives, carrying a big wooden pestle and mortar. Nissia doesn't smile much, but today she's grinning broadly. I scowl at her. Mama wraps the sorghum in a clean capulana and helps me to balance the bundle on my head.

"Off you go — and don't waste any time. He'll be here soon!"

I feel a smile as big as Nissia's spread across my face. It's today! Today, Josias is coming home. Nissia and I almost run down to the river, despite the heavy loads on our heads. Usually, we stop and greet our neighbours politely as we pass them working in their fields, but today they shake their heads as we dash past: "Children today have no respect for their elders."

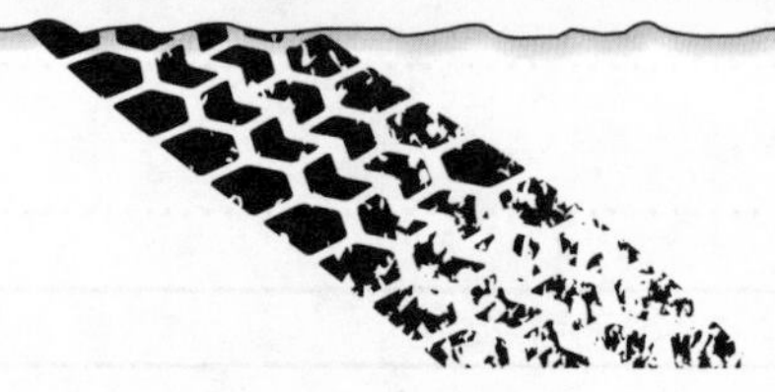

By the time we reach the river, the sun's up and we can hear the cockerels crowing in the village. Every time I hear a motorbike on the road, I look up to see if it's him. Nissia helps me pour the sorghum into the mortar and I pound it with the heavy pestle until my arms feel like porridge. If I pound faster, maybe Josias will arrive sooner. Nissia scoops the grains into a basket and rinses them in the river.

The sun's higher still. What if Josias arrives and we're not there to greet him? He must have experienced so many new things in the city. Has he missed us, or will the village seem tedious to him now?

"Let's go, Mira," Nissia says. Her smile has disappeared again. "Don't drop any of the sorghum! They can't have the ceremony without it."

The neighbours, now pausing to cook cassava at the edge of their field, laugh at us as we totter past with our precious cargo.

Mama is a whirlwind, simultaneously trying to sweep the yard and give Olga and Dinoka a bath. She wordlessly hands each of us an empty bucket and whisks the sorghum away. We take the buckets along to the pump, dawdling now because it's hot and we're exhausted.

Aunty Marlene is at the pump, washing her feet.

"The bus from Nampula has already been past," she cackles.
"There's no sign of your brother. He won't come today after all."

Then I hear it — the throaty roar of a motorbike engine. I hold my breath.

sorghum — a type of grain
capulana — colourful printed cloth
cassava — a vegetable like a potato

Written by Katharine Howell

Consider

What do you think will happen as soon as Josias arrives?
Think about what Mira will do, and how she will react.

It's Today — Question Set 1

1 **Why does Mira pretend to be asleep?** 2D

....

2 **Draw lines to match the person (on the left) with their relationship to Mira (on the right).** 2B

Olga	cousin
Marlene	sister
Nissia	niece
Dinoka	brother
Josias	aunty

Scan the text for each of the names, and then read around the name to find out how they are related to Mira.

3 **Complete the table by writing words from the second page of the text next to their definitions.** 2A

Word from text	Definition
....	boring
....	at the same time
....	taking time

4 **Why are the words *sorghum*, *capulana* and *cassava* and their definitions given in the box at the end of the text?** 2F

....

....

5 **Read these statements carefully, then use the text to decide whether they are true or false.** 2B

	True	False
Mira shares a bed with other members of her family.	☐	☐
Mira carries the grain on her head down to the river.	☐	☐
Mira washes the grain in the river while Nissia watches.	☐	☐
The girls meet Josias at the pump.	☐	☐

6 **a) What type of language feature is used in this phrase: *...so that the grains break off the stems, dancing everywhere*? Circle the correct word.** 2G

simile personification

metaphor

b) What does the phrase *dancing everywhere* suggest about the grains? 2G

....

....

What do you picture when you read that sentence?

It's Today — Question Set 2

1. **Find and copy three pieces of evidence from the text which show that the story is from another culture.** 2D

1. ....

2. ....

3. ....

2. **a) Why do Nissia and Mira *almost run down to the river*?** 2D

....

Don't just guess at the answer. Read the sentences before this quote in the text.

Who? What? Where? When? Why?

b) What is the difference in the way they return home? Why do you think this is? 2H

....

....

c) What word in the text shows they know how important the grain is? 2A

....

3. **Give two pieces of evidence from the text which show that Mira is really looking forward to her brother (Josias) coming home.** 2D

1. ....

....

2. ....

....

4 Read the paragraph that begins *The sun's higher still*. Why do you think Mira asks herself the questions in this paragraph? 2D

....

....

5 What metaphor on the second page shows how busy Mira's mother is in preparing for Josias's return? 2G

....

A metaphor is when something is described as something it is not.

Challenge

Lucky Mira having all that family! They all seem really friendly.

Tick a box to show if you agree or disagree with the pig. Then complete the table to show what you think.

Agree ☐ Disagree ☐

What I think:	....
Why I think this:	....
Evidence from the text:	....

2D

The Sealed Room

Arthur Conan Doyle created the famous fictional detective Sherlock Holmes, but also wrote other stories of mystery and adventure. The following extract is taken from his short story *The Sealed Room* which is about a house with a room which has been mysteriously sealed up, with nobody able to get inside. Here, Mr Stanniford, the new owner of the house, and his friends, Mr Adler (who is the narrator of the story) and Perceval (who works as a banker's clerk) attempt to open the sealed room for the first time.

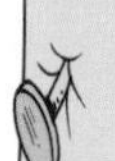

The banker's clerk took up the lamp and led the way. But he paused in the passage outside the door, and his hand was shaking, so that the light flickered up and down the high, bare walls.

"Mr. Stanniford," said he, in a cracking voice, "I hope you will prepare yourself in case any shock should be awaiting you when that seal is removed and the door is opened."

"What could there be, Perceval? You are trying to frighten me."

"No, Mr. Stanniford; but I should wish you to be ready... to be braced up... not to allow yourself..." He had to lick his dry lips between every jerky sentence, and I suddenly realised, as clearly as if he had told me, that he knew what was behind that closed door, and that it was something terrible. "Here are the keys, Mr. Stanniford, but remember my warning!"

He had a bunch of assorted keys in his hand, and the young man snatched them from him. Then he thrust a knife under the discoloured seal and jerked it off. The lamp was rattling and shaking in Perceval's hands, so I took it from him and held it near the key hole, while Stanniford tried key after key. At last one turned in the lock, the door flew open, he took one step into the room, and then, with a horrible cry, the young man fell senseless at our feet.

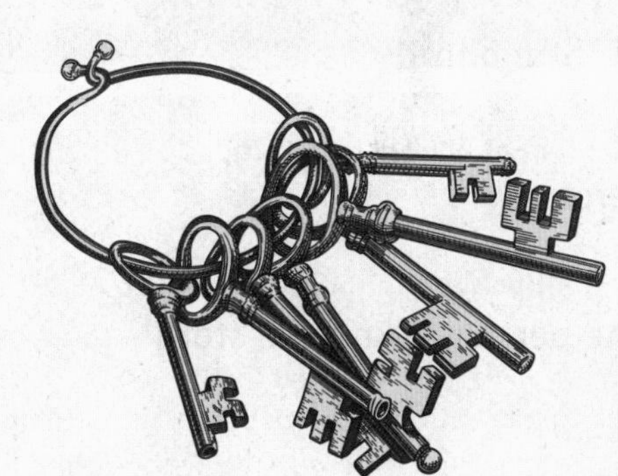

If I had not given heed to the clerk's warning, and braced myself for a shock, I should certainly have dropped the lamp. The room, windowless and bare, was fitted up as a photographic laboratory, with a tap and sink at the side of it. A shelf of bottles and measures stood at one side, and a peculiar, heavy smell, partly chemical, partly animal, filled the air. A single table and chair were in front of us, and at this, with his back turned towards us, a man was seated in the act of writing. His outline and attitude were as natural as life; but as the light fell upon him, it made my hair rise to see that the nape of his neck was black and wrinkled, and no thicker than my wrist. Dust lay upon him — thick, yellow dust — upon his hair, his shoulders, his shrivelled, lemon-coloured hands. His head had fallen forward upon his breast. His pen still rested upon a discoloured sheet of paper.

An extract from *The Sealed Room* by Arthur Conan Doyle.

Consider

What have they discovered behind the sealed door?
Write down <u>what</u> you think, and <u>why</u> you think it.

The Sealed Room — Question Set 1

1 **Who *led the way* in the first paragraph?** 2B

Tick one box

Mr Stanniford	☐
Perceval	☐
The person telling the story	☐

If none of the answers fit, you may need to read more of the text.

2 **What reason does the banker's clerk give for telling Mr Stanniford he needs to prepare himself?** 2B

....

....

3 **Draw lines to match the first half of the sentence (on the left) to an accurate second half (on the right).** 2C

Perceval (the banker's clerk)	had been in the sealed room for a long time.
The man, who was sitting at the table,	held the lamp close to the key hole.
The man, who unlocked the door,	knew what was within the sealed room.
The person who is telling the story	cried out when he saw the dead man.

Do the ones you're really sure of first. Then you can use a process of elimination to help you with the others. Remember to keep looking back at the text!

4 **What was the difference between how Mr Stanniford (the young man) reacted to what he saw in the sealed room and how the person who is telling the story reacted?** 2H

....

....

5 **Draw lines to match each word from the text (on the left) to a word (on the right) which could replace it.** 2A

cracking	stained
dry	steadied
discoloured	breaking
braced	withered
shrivelled	parched

It really helps to read the whole sentence with the new word to see if it makes sense.

6 **Number these events in the order they happen in the extract.** 2C

Various different keys were tried in the lock.	
The seal was removed from the lock.	
A group of men approached the sealed room.	1
Mr Stanniford was warned of what he might discover.	
The inside of the room revealed a photographic laboratory and a dead man.	

Find and underline the events in the text. Number them in the text. Then match each event in the question to the numbered event in the text.

The Sealed Room — Question Set 2

1 **How do you know the passageway they are walking along is dark?** 2D

....

For these two questions, you'll need to think about what the characters say and do.

2 **Find and copy two pieces of evidence that show how nervous the banker's clerk is feeling.** 2D

1. ....

2. ....

3 **Read up to ...*the young man fell senseless at our feet.* Which of the following statements are true and which are false?** 2B

	True	False
Mr Stanniford was feeling impatient.	☐	☐
No one knew what was behind the sealed door.	☐	☐
Mr Stanniford knew which key to use.	☐	☐
The door was only sealed by a lock.	☐	☐

You'll need to do a bit of digging beneath the surface of the text to infer whether each statement is true or false. Take your time with questions like this!

4) a) Read the description of the sealed room in the final paragraph of the text. Write down an adjective which does not appear in the text to describe what the sealed room is like.

2C

....

b) What evidence is there to support your choice of word?

2F

....

....

....

5) Find two examples which tell us the dead man has been there a very long time.

2D

1. ....

2. ....

You are providing evidence so you'll need to find it then copy it carefully.

Challenge

This newspaper report is most frightening. What a terrible shock it must have been to discover that poor man!

Can you explain to the rabbit why this is **NOT** a newspaper report? Say what type of text it is and how you know this based on the features it does or does not have.

....

....

....

....

....

2F

Fairtrade Bananas

Do you like bananas? If so, you're not alone. On average, each person in the UK eats a whopping 100 bananas a year. In this text, a campaigner argues that choosing Fairtrade bananas improves people's lives in other parts of the world.

The ultimate convenience food

Individually packaged in their skins and incredibly healthy, bananas are a superb snack. Also, costing as little as 11p each, they're very affordable. However, would you enjoy them as much if you knew that the people growing them were being unfairly treated? That their health was suffering and their children were going hungry? Or are you prepared to pay a little extra so that the producers can escape poverty?

Where do our bananas come from?

Although bananas are enjoyed all around the world, they grow best in tropical regions close to the equator, where the temperature is a balmy 27°C on average. Many developing countries are located in these regions and the banana trade is hugely important for people's livelihoods.

In the past, most of our bananas were grown on small family farms in the Windward Islands in the Caribbean. At one time, 50% of the population were employed in banana production, and the Islands relied on the money from exporting bananas to the UK for health, education and many other things that we take for granted in the UK. However, more than four fifths of banana farmers have been forced out of business, causing huge unemployment and plunging families into poverty.

This is because UK supermarkets can now buy bananas more cheaply from large plantations, such as those in Ecuador, Costa Rica, and Ivory Coast in West Africa. It's cheaper to grow bananas on large plantations because fewer workers are needed. Also, the giant companies that own them can invest in technology for irrigation and packing.

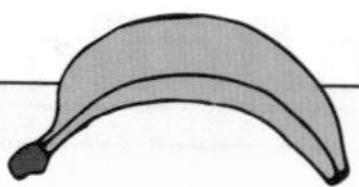

Plantation Problems

These huge plantations often use lots of agrochemicals, which pollute water supplies, killing fish and coral reefs. The chemicals are sprayed by planes and fall, not just on the crops, but on workers too, causing terrible health problems, such as cancer and respiratory diseases. If this isn't bad enough, workers often work 14 hour days, 6 days a week, in terrible heat, but still don't earn enough to pay for essentials such as housing and food. This is what has to be done to produce bananas for the price supermarkets are willing to pay, so that they can lure in customers with bargain prices. But is it really a price worth paying for 30p off a bunch of bananas?

The methods of banana production used in small farms are far less damaging to the environment. However, these farmers simply cannot produce bananas as cheaply as the giant plantations and so have largely been pushed out the market.

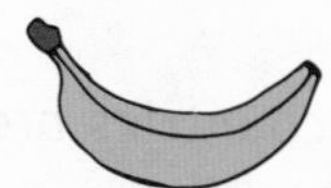

Buy Fairtrade Bananas

Luckily for the Windward Islands, the Fairtrade Foundation has stepped in to support small-scale banana producers. They make sure farmers get a decent price for their bananas and that workers get a fair wage and safe conditions. In addition, for every box of bananas sold, the community gets the Fairtrade Premium. This is used to improve the lives of local people, for example, by paying for health checks, or for a pre-school.

One in three bananas bought in the UK is Fairtrade. This makes a huge difference to people's lives. However, it could be higher. What will you choose next time you go shopping? To save a few pence, or to make sure producers aren't exploited?

Written by Sharon Keeley-Holden

Discuss

Use the section 'Plantation Problems' to make a list of all the problems created by banana plantations. Discuss with a partner whether the impact of each problem is <u>environmental</u>, <u>economic</u> or <u>human</u>.

Fairtrade Bananas — Question Set 1

1 **Why does the author want people to choose Fairtrade bananas?** 2B

....

2 **Complete this sentence correctly.**
'Bananas grow best in tropical regions because...' 2B

Tick one box

...that's where the banana trade is the greatest. ☐

...they are enjoyed all around the world. ☐

...they are close to the equator and the temperature is 27°C. ☐

...that's where the developing countries are. ☐

To find the answer, scan the text for the words 'tropical regions'.

3 **What is the main purpose of this text?** 2C

Tick one box

To explain how Fairtrade bananas are grown. ☐

To describe the health benefits of Fairtrade bananas. ☐

To explain the journey Fairtrade bananas make from the plant to our homes. ☐

To persuade people to buy Fairtrade bananas. ☐

This is a 'summarising' question. You need to think about what the whole text is about, not just what parts of the text are about.

4 **Find and copy one phrase from the paragraph 'Plantation Problems' which shows the impact of chemicals on the workers' health.** 2A

....

....

5 **Read the following sentences carefully and use the text to decide whether they are true or false. Tick your answers.** 2B

	True	False
The Caribbean Islands used to grow most of the UK's bananas.	☐	☐
Bananas can be grown more cheaply on large plantations because more workers are needed.	☐	☐
Workers on large plantations earn a lot of money.	☐	☐
The Windward Islands have been helped by the Fairtrade Foundation.	☐	☐

6 **In texts like this, statistics (facts including numbers) are often used to support the writing. Find and copy two examples of statistics in the text.** 2G

1. ....

....

2. ....

....

To answer this type of question, it might help to scan the text for numbers.

Fairtrade Bananas — Question Set 2

(1) **Why does the first subheading describe bananas as *The ultimate convenience food?* Give at least two reasons.** 2D

....

....

(2) **a) Find and copy two examples of rhetorical questions in the text.** 2F

1. ....

....

2. ....

....

A rhetorical question is one that does not expect an answer.

b) What is the purpose of asking rhetorical questions in this type of text? 2F

....

....

(3) **Find and copy two phrases from the section '*Where do our bananas come from?*' that show how much people in developing countries depend on the banana trade.** 2D

1. ....

....

2. ....

....

4 Read the paragraph that begins *'In the past...'*. What is the effect of using the word *plunging* to describe how families became poor? 2G

....

5 Draw lines to match the words from the text (on the left) with their definitions (on the right). 2A

irrigation	the state of being very poor
exploited	the people who live somewhere
poverty	the supply of water to land to help growth of crops
community	used unfairly

Challenge

I don't understand why I have to buy Fairtrade bananas. Aren't all bananas the same?

Give three reasons why it is a good idea to buy Fairtrade wherever possible, using evidence from the text to support your answer.

Reasons for buying Fairtrade:	Evidence from the text:
1.	....
2.	....
3.	....

2D

A Crow and a Scarecrow

A narrative poem is a poem that tells a story. This narrative poem by Carol Ann Duffy tells the story of an unlikely relationship between a crow and a scarecrow.

A crow and a scarecrow fell in love
out in the fields.
The scarecrow's heart was a stuffed leather glove
but his love was real.
The crow perched on the stick of a wrist
and opened her beak:
Scarecrow, I love you madly, deeply.
Speak.

Crow; rasped the Scarecrow, *hear these words*
from my straw throat.
I love you too
from my boot to my hat
by way of my old tweed coat.
Croak.
The crow crowed back,
Scarecrow, let me take you away
to live in a tall tree.
I'll be a true crow wife to you
if you'll marry me.

The Scarecrow considered.
Crow, tell me how
a groom with a broomstick spine
can take a bride.
I know you believe in the love
in these button eyes
but I'm straw inside
and straw can't fly.

The crow pecked at his heart
with her beak
then flapped away,
and back and forth she flew to him
all day, all day,
until she pulled one last straw
from his tattered vest
and soared across the sun with it
to her new nest.

And there she slept, high in her tree,
winged, in a bed of love.
Night fell.
The slow moon rose
over a meadow,
a heap of clothes,
two boots,
an empty glove.

Carol Ann Duffy

Consider

Consider how the scarecrow's existence changes from the start to the end of the poem. Where does he end up? Discuss your ideas with a partner.

A Crow and a Scarecrow — Question Set 1

1 **Read these statements carefully and decide if they are true or false. Tick your answers.** 2B

	True	False
The scarecrow wore leather gloves.	☐	☐
The crow and the scarecrow declare their love for each other.	☐	☐
The scarecrow is wearing a coat and a hat.	☐	☐
The crow pecks out the scarecrow's eyes.	☐	☐
The crow keeps returning to the scarecrow.	☐	☐

When you scan the text, remember to start from the beginning, not half way through.

2 **What has the poet used to show when either the crow or the scarecrow speaks?** 2F

....

3 **Why does the scarecrow think that getting married is not going to be possible?** 2B

....

....

4 **Draw lines to match each verse with the correct summary.** 2C

Verse 1	A discussion between the crow and the scarecrow.
Verse 2	The crow takes pieces of straw from the scarecrow.
Verse 3	An introduction to the crow and the scarecrow in the field.
Verse 4	The scarecrow explaining why they can't get married.
Verse 5	A description of the scarecrow with no more straw in him.

You don't have to match them in order (Verse 1, then Verse 2...). Match the ones you are most sure of first.

5 **Give one word from the text which describes how the crow flies?** 2A

....

6 **Which of the following statements best describes the rhyming structure of this poem? Tick your answer.** 2H

ABABABAB ☐ AABBAABB ☐

Free verse (no rhyming pattern) ☐ A different rhyming pattern for each verse ☐

Lines with the same letter rhyme. See page 9 for a reminder of how rhyme schemes work.

A Crow and a Scarecrow — Question Set 2

1. **In the introduction to the text, it says the relationship between the crow and the scarecrow is an unlikely one. Why do you think this is?** 2D

....

2. **Why do you think the poet chose the word *rasped* to describe the way the scarecrow speaks?** 2G

....

....

3. **Read the definitions of the terms below, then draw lines to match the phrases from the poem with the correct term.** 2G

Alliteration: words that are close together beginning with the same consonant sound.

Assonance: words that are close together containing the same vowel sound.

Semirhyme: when part of one word rhymes with another word.

'soared across the sun'	semirhyme
'a stuffed leather glove'	assonance
'a groom with a broomstick spine'	alliteration

Sometimes, two different letters can make the same vowel sound.

Dictionary

4 Find and copy two phrases from the fourth verse of the poem that show the scarecrow is going to be left in a bad state.

In questions like this, you need to copy the exact words from the text carefully.

2D

1. ....

2. ....

5 At the end of the poem, why is there a heap of clothes left on the ground?

2D

....

....

6 Why do you think the poet describes the crow's nest as a *bed of love* in the last verse?

2G

....

....

Challenge

The scarecrow must be pretty angry with the crow, leaving him in a heap on the ground!

Tick a box to show whether you agree or disagree with the elephant. Then give a reason for your answer, supported by evidence from the text.

Agree ☐ Disagree ☐

....

....

....

2D

Answers

Text 1 — Poetry

Pages 6 and 7: Daffodils — Question Set 1

1. You should have ticked: a cloud
2. You should have matched these phrases:
   the cloud — above the hills
   the daffodils — under the trees
   the stars — on the Milky Way
   the waves — next to the daffodils
3. Any two of the following examples:
   I saw a crowd, dancing in the breeze, Tossing their heads, in sprightly dance, they/Out-did the sparkling waves in glee, In such a jocund company
4. You should have ticked: cheerful
5. The poet feels happy when he thinks about the daffodils — the text says 'And then my heart with pleasure fills'.
6. You should have given the events the following numbers:
   The poet describes numerous rows of daffodils moving. — 2
   The poet recalls the pleasing sight of the daffodils. — 4
   The poet describes his first sighting of the daffodils. — 1
   The poet compares the daffodils to the beauty of the water. — 3

Pages 8 and 9: Daffodils — Question Set 2

1. You should have ticked 'lonely as a cloud' and 'Continuous as the stars that shine'
2. a) You could have circled any one of the words in the list.
   b) Your answer must explain how the poet feels and use quotes from the poem in support.
   Example:
   I think the poet feels heartened by seeing the daffodils. At the start of the poem he is 'lonely as a cloud' but by the end of the third verse, he says 'a poet could not but be gay' meaning they would make any poet happy.
3. You should have matched these phrases:
   host — group
   margin — narrow strip
   sprightly — energetic
   pensive — thoughtful
   bliss — happiness
4. Example:
   The poet describes both the daffodils and the waves as dancing but he suggests the daffodils are much happier and better at dancing than the waves when he says 'but they/Out-did the sparkling waves in glee'.
5. You should have ticked: ABABCC

Challenge:
Your answer could have made the following or similar points:
The poet has used personification to describe the daffodils' movement. When he says 'dancing in the breeze', he means they were moving from side to side, as if they were dancing.

Text 2 — Newspaper Article

Pages 12 and 13: Winter Paralympics — Question Set 1

1. You should have ticked:
   To share the success of the South Korea Winter Paralympics.
2. He won his 13th Paralympic gold — he's the most decorated Canadian Paralympian of all time.
3. You should have matched these pairs:
   China — will host the Winter Paralympics next time
   Slovakia — will welcome home a Paralympian who has won 4 golds and 1 silver
   South Korea — held the most watched Winter Paralympics to date
   Canada — has produced the most successful cross-country Paralympian of all time
   Tajikistan — took part in the 2018 Winter Paralympics for the first time
4. 1994 China — false
   2006 Turin — true
   2018 South Korea — true
   2022 Lillehammer — false
5. Any three of the following:
   biggest games, most watched, most tickets sold, larger audience, more athletes, more countries, a greater percentage of countries winning at least one medal
6. You should have matched these pairs:
   '... and 26 out of the 49 countries taking part won at least one medal.' — facts and figures
   'Country debuts and first gold medals' — subheading
   'Winter Paralympics: the best bits from the Pyeongchang Games' — headline
   'Fitzpatrick said she wanted to celebrate with a "proper cup of English tea".' — quote

Pages 14 and 15: Winter Paralympics — Question Set 2

1. Example:
   They suggest that there were many more highlights than those mentioned in this report.
2. You should have ticked: successful
3. Example:
   It means that she hasn't had a cup of tea that has tasted like English tea whilst being in South Korea.
4. You should have given the athletes/countries the following numbers:
   Henrieta Farkasova — 2
   Team GB — 1
   Menna Fitzpatrick — 3
   Millie Knight — 4

Answers

5. Any three of the following phrases:
   boasting of a successful Games
   Records set for Paralympics GB
   hit their medal target
   winning Britain's gold medal
   she wanted to celebrate
   the most decorated British Winter Paralympian of all-time

Challenge

Any four of the following phrases:
'biggest and most watched edition to date'
'the 12th Winter Paralympics'
'it's traditional for every Games to be hailed'
'number of tickets sold exceeded those sold at Sochi'
audience 'tripling since the 2006 Turin edition'
'in his fifth appearance at the Games'
'more athletes taking part from more countries than ever before'
'a higher percentage than at any Paralympics since Lillehammer in 1994'
'The seven medals won was one more than in Sochi'

Text 3 — Children's Fiction

Pages 18 and 19: Conker — Question Set 1

1. To pick up conkers
2. Any three of the following examples:
   tyres, (piles of) cars, a hut, potholes, muddy tracks, conkers, a guard dog, a metal stake, rusting wrecks
3. You should have ticked:
   He is fastened to a post by a chain.
   A chain is wrapped around his hind legs.
4. the same gentle brown eyes, the same way of holding his head on one side (when he was thinking), he likes jelly babies
5. You should have given the events the following numbers:
   Nick rubbed the dog until he was warmer. — 5
   The dog ate the jelly babies one by one. — 3
   Nick heard the noise of a dog in pain. — 2
   The dog was untangled from the chain. — 4
   Nick climbed into the yard. — 1
6. Example:
   This means that Nick is being cautious/safe/careful about the dog because even though he looks friendly, he might bark, bite or lash out.

Pages 20 and 21: Conker — Question Set 2

1. Example:

What I think:	Nick was fond of dogs.
Evidence from the text:	Nick used to have a pet dog so we definitely know he was fond of dogs.

   You could also have said:
   What I think: Nick was curious to find out more.
   Evidence: Nick was definitely curious about the noise because he was going to leave at first and then he changed his mind. / He kept moving through the yard until he found the dog and then he stayed to find out if he was friendly (like Old Station).
   What I think: Nick could tell something was in pain.
   Evidence: Nick could tell something was in pain because the text says 'whine and whimper and yelp' and 'pitiful howling'.
2. It suggests the tyres were all scattered around the yard in a messy way.
3. unselfish
4. a) You could have ticked either option for this question.
   b) Example answers:
   If you ticked yes: I think Nick will bring someone back because he tells the dog that he's coming back. He needs the help of someone else (probably an adult) to do more to help the dog.
   If you ticked no: I think Nick won't tell someone what he's found because he shouldn't have been in the yard in the first place. He will want to keep it a secret so he doesn't get into trouble.
5. You should have given an explanation that covers the following points:
   I think the story is called 'Conker' because when Nick was looking for conkers he came across this dog. I think that further on in the text, Nick will call the dog 'Conker'.

Challenge:

Your answer should be backed up by a valid reason and evidence.
Examples:
What: I think Nick should have left the yard.
Why: The yard seems like a dangerous place to be.
Evidence: There are 'Great piles of cars towered all about him'
OR
What: I think Nick was right to help the dog.
Why: The dog is being mistreated.
Evidence: The dog is 'thin' and has 'sores around his neck'.

Answers

Text 4 — Myth

Pages 24 and 25: The Coming of Raven — Question Set 1

1. The Inuits are from the Arctic regions of Canada, Greenland and Alaska. — true
   The Earth and the Sun were created by the Inuit people. — false
   Needles were made from the bones of animals. — true
   Raven was always pleased with the actions of the Inuit people. — false
2. plunged
3. see, keep warm, hunt
4. He was worried that his father would be angry with him for looking at the sun.
5. You should have given the events the following numbers:
   Raven Boy fled to the other side of the universe. — 4
   Raven took pity on the people for the first time. — 3
   Raven created day and night and summer and winter. — 6
   Raven took pity on the people for the second time. — 5
   Raven took the sun away. — 2
6. You should have matched these words:
   plundered — robbed
   companion — friend
   implored — begged
   honoured — respected

Pages 26 and 27: The Coming of Raven — Question Set 2

1. Example:
   The people had forgotten their promise to only kill what they need — they only cared about themselves and not the Earth. Raven was cross with them and so he took away the sun to teach them a lesson.
2. There are lots of possible answers to this question.
   Examples:
   'He soared towards the sun, grabbed it, stuffed it into the bag'
   'and uncovered the sun for a few days'
   'Sometimes, Raven showed his son the caribou skin bag and the sun inside it'
   'and flung the sun spinning across the sky'
3. a) You should have ticked: He is afraid of him.
   b) Example:
   In the text, it says Raven Boy is 'Fearful of his father's anger' and he flees to the other side of the universe to avoid being told off by his father.
4. You should have ticked:
   disobedient - unhappy - respectful
5. Example:
   The author uses personification to show the reader how much the Earth was suffering due to the Inuits' behaviour.

Challenge

Examples:
(good leader) Good because I think Raven would do anything to protect the Earth from harm — he made the people promise not to kill more than they needed. He punished the people for a good reason but he also showed kindness and understanding by giving them back the sun for a few days to hunt.
(bad leader) Bad because every time he took away the sun he was actually punishing the Earth as things began to die. He was indecisive when he kept feeling sorry for the Inuit people and I don't think a leader should be like that.
(both good and bad leader) Good and bad because he looked after the Earth and tried to teach the Inuit people how to be better but he shouldn't have tempted his son by showing him the sun in the bag. He obviously didn't want to damage the Earth, as he says, 'Bring back the sun, or the world I created will die!'. And he was clever because he created night and day, summer and winter.

Text 5 — Explanation Text

Pages 30 and 31: Helicopters — Question Set 1

1. improbable
2. a) You should have labelled the diagram like this:

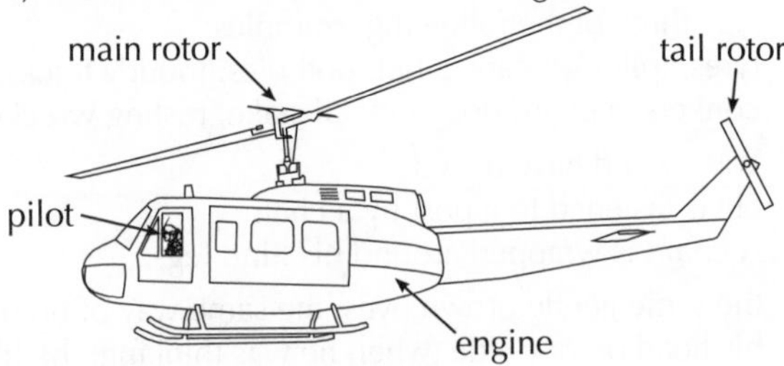

   b) You should have matched these pairs:
   main rotor — spins quickly to create lift
   engine — powers the rotors
   tail rotor — balances the forces acting on the helicopter
   pilot — steers the helicopter by tilting the blades
3. About 500 rotations per minute
4. You should have numbered the statements like this:
   The internal combustion engine was invented. — 3
   Leonardo da Vinci designed a spiral-shaped airscrew. — 2
   The world's first helicopter took flight. — 4
   Children in China played with bamboo-copters. — 1
5. You should have ticked: He designed the VS-300.
6. You should have written: 'If it only had one rotor'

Pages 32 and 33: Helicopters — Question Set 2

1. Example: To explain what the next part of the text is going to be about and answer the question.
2. It is easier for a helicopter to fly on Mars than on Earth. — false
   The Halo helicopter is larger than the VS-300 helicopter — true

Answers

The blades on a helicopter are motionless like the wings on a plane. — false

3. (scientists and engineers in Europe were) inspired by these bamboo blades.
4. Example: It helps the reader imagine what the weight is like (as many people wouldn't know how heavy 56 tonnes is).
5. Example: It was used as a starting point for building helicopters. OR It was like a foundation.

Challenge

You could have agreed or disagreed with the dog.
Example:
Disagree.
What you think about the first flight — I think the flight was really important to the development of the helicopter.
Why you think this — It was the basis for the first mass-produced helicopters. Without it, the helicopter might not have developed into the helicopter we have now, which has so many purposes.

Text 6 — Story from Another Culture

Pages 36 and 37: It's Today — Question Set 1

1. It's early so she doesn't want to get up.
2. You should have matched these pairs:
   Olga — sister
   Marlene — aunty
   Nissia — cousin
   Dinoka — niece
   Josias — brother
3. You should have filled in the table like this:

Word from text	Definition
tedious	boring
simultaneously	at the same time
dawdling	taking time

4. Example: The words may be unfamiliar to the reader. / They are unusual words.
5. Mira shares a bed with other members of her family. — true
   Mira carries the grain on her head down to the river. — true
   Mira washes the grain in the river while Nissia watches. — false
   The girls meet Josias at the pump. — false
6. a) You should have circled: personification
   b) Example: They are moving and jumping about.

Pages 38 and 39: It's Today — Question Set 2

1. Your answer should have mentioned 3 of the following:
   • they have mosquito nets over their beds
   • the different types of food, e.g. sorghum, cassava
   • they carry bundles on their heads
   • they collect water from a pump
   • they wash the grain in the river
   • their names are unusual
2. a) They are excited about Josias coming home.
   b) Example: When they leave the river, they have to go carefully and slowly because they don't want to lose any of the sorghum that they have just ground down and washed.
   c) precious
3. Your answer should mention two of the following:
   • She has a big smile on her face.
   • She exclaims 'It's today!'.
   • They run to the river.
   • She pounds the grain fast to get back quicker.
   • Every time she hears a motorcycle she looks up to see if it's him.
   • She worries that they might not be there to greet him.
   • She holds her breath when she hears the motorcycle at the end of the text.
4. Because she is worried / wants everything to be just right when he arrives.
5. 'Mama is a whirlwind'

Challenge

Answers should be based on what has happened in this extract. Example:
Disagree.
What I think — I don't think everyone is friendly.
Why I think this — There are moments in the story when Nissia and Aunty Marlene are not very friendly.
Evidence from the text — The text says that 'Nissia doesn't smile much'. When Aunty Marlene tells Mira her brother isn't coming 'she cackles', which shows she's laughing unkindly and taking pleasure in what she's saying.

Text 7 — Classic Fiction

Pages 42 and 43: The Sealed Room — Question Set 1

1. You should have ticked: Perceval
2. Example:
   In case there is something shocking behind the door
3. You should have made these sentences:
   Perceval (the banker's clerk) knew what was within the sealed room.
   The man, who was sitting at the table, had been in the sealed room for a long time.
   The man, who unlocked the door, cried out when he saw the dead man.
   The person who is telling the story held the lamp close to the key hole.
4. Mr Stanniford cried out and fell to the floor but the person telling the story stayed calm and prepared himself for the shock.
5. You should have matched these words:
   cracking — breaking
   dry — parched
   discoloured — stained
   braced — steadied
   shrivelled — withered

Answers

6. You should have given the events the following numbers:
Various different keys were tried in the lock. — 4
The seal was removed from the lock. — 3
Mr Stanniford was warned of what he might discover. — 2
The inside of the room revealed a photographic laboratory and a dead man. — 5

Pages 44 and 45: The Sealed Room — Question Set 2

1. The banker's clerk is carrying a lamp.
2. Any two of the following examples:
his hand was shaking, he spoke in a cracking voice, he had to lick his dry lips, his sentences were jerky, the lamp rattled and shook in his hands
3. You should have ticked the following for the sentences:
Mr Stanniford was feeling impatient. — true
No one knew what was behind the sealed door. — false
Mr Stanniford knew which key to use. — false
The door was only sealed by a lock. — false
4. a) Any appropriate adjective, as long as in part b) you can give evidence for your choice, for example 'spooky'.
b) Your answer should refer to the text.
Example:
I think the author has made the room seem spooky because of the strange smell, the equipment that is there and the dead body! It says in the text 'the nape of his neck was black and wrinkled'.
5. Any two of the following examples:
there is thick yellow dust on him, the paper is discoloured, the nape of his neck was black and wrinkled, the neck was no thicker than the narrator's wrist, he had shrivelled lemon-coloured hands.

Challenge
Example:
This is not a newspaper report because it doesn't have a headline or any subheadings. It is not reporting the death, it is telling the story of discovering the man. It is more like a detective story and it is being told in the first person 'If I had not given heed...'. In newspapers the first paragraph usually tells the reader what, where, when and who.

Text 8 — Persuasive Text

Pages 48 and 49: Fairtrade Bananas — Question Set 1

1. To improve people's lives in other parts of the world.
2. You should have ticked: ...they are close to the equator and the temperature is 27°.
3. You should have ticked: To persuade people to buy Fairtrade bananas.
4. 'causing terrible health problems (such as cancer and respiratory diseases)'
5. The Caribbean Islands used to grow most of the UK's bananas. — true
Bananas can be grown more cheaply on large plantations because more workers are needed. — false
Workers on large plantations earn a lot of money. — false
The Windward Islands have been helped by the Fairtrac Foundation. — true
6. Your answer could have mentioned any two of the following:
• 'costing as little as 11p each'
• 'the temperature is a balmy 27°C on average'
• 'At one time 50% of the population were employed i banana production'
• 'more than four fifths of banana farmers have been forced out of business'
• 'workers often work 14 hour days, 6 days a week, in terrible heat'
• 'One in three bananas bought in the UK is Fairtrade'

Pages 50 and 51: Fairtrade Bananas — Question Set 2

1. Your answer should mention at least two of the following: 'Individually packaged in their skins', 'incredibly healthy', 'very affordable'.
2. a) Examples:
• 'However, would you enjoy them as much if you knew that the people growing them were being unfairly treated?'
• 'Or are you prepared to pay a little extra so that the producers can escape poverty?'
b) They are asked to make the reader think about their own opinions.
3. 'is hugely important for people's livelihoods' AND 'the Islands relied on the money from exporting bananas to the UK for health, education...'
4. Example: It means it happened very quickly and they fe deeply into poverty.
5. You should have matched these pairs:
irrigation — the supply of water to land to help growth of crops
exploited — used unfairly
poverty — the state of being very poor
community — the people who live somewhere

Challenge
Examples:
Reason: Farmers will get a good price for their bananas.
Evidence: 'They make sure farmers get a decent price'
OR
Reason: Workers will be paid fairly.
Evidence: 'workers get a fair wage'
OR
Reason: Workers will be kept safe.
Evidence: 'safe conditions'
OR
Reason: Additional money will be used to improve lives, e.g. health checks, pre-schools.
Evidence: 'the community gets the Fairtrade Premium. This is used to improve the lives of local people'

Answers

OR
Reason: The environment will be looked after.
Evidence: 'far less damaging to the environment'
OR
Reason: Improves people's lives in other parts of the world.
Evidence: 'makes a huge difference to people's lives'

Text 9 — Narrative Poetry

Pages 54 and 55: A Crow and a Scarecrow — Question Set 1

1. The scarecrow wore leather gloves. — false
   The crow and the scarecrow declare their love for each other. — true
   The scarecrow is wearing a coat and a hat. — true
   The crow pecks out the scarecrow's eyes. — false
   The crow keeps returning to the scarecrow. — true
2. The poet has used italics.
3. He's made of wood and straw and cannot fly.
4. You should have matched these pairs:
   Verse 1 — An introduction to the crow and the scarecrow in the field.
   Verse 2 — A discussion between the crow and the scarecrow.
   Verse 3 — The scarecrow explaining why they can't get married.
   Verse 4 — The crow takes pieces of straw from the scarecrow.
   Verse 5 — A description of the scarecrow with no more straw in him.
5. 'soared' OR 'flapped'
6. You should have ticked: 'A different rhyming pattern for each verse'

Pages 56 and 57: A Crow and a Scarecrow — Question Set 2

1. Example: Scarecrows are there to scare away crows.
2. Example: The scarecrow is made of straw, so its throat will be very dry.
3. You should have matched these pairs:
   '<u>s</u>oared across the <u>s</u>un' — alliteration
   'a st<u>u</u>ffed leather gl<u>o</u>ve' — assonance
   'a gr<u>oom</u> with a br<u>oom</u>stick spine' — semirhyme
   (It would also be correct to match this last phrase to 'assonance'.)
4. 'The crow pecked at his heart', 'one last straw from his tattered vest'
5. The crow has taken all the straw which was inside the clothes to make up the scarecrow.
6. Example: The crow loves the scarecrow, so by making her nest from the scarecrow's straw, she makes a 'bed of love'.

Challenge

Disagree — The scarecrow loved the crow but couldn't marry her because 'straw can't fly'. The crow enables the straw to fly up to her tree, so they can live together in a 'bed of love'.

Acknowledgements
p.10-11: Article reproduced with permission from © Copyright Guardian News & Media Ltd 2019
p.10-11: Photos © Maddie Meyer/Staff/Getty Images Sport
p.16-17: From Of Lions and Unicorns by Michael Morpurgo. HarperCollins 2013
p.22-23: From The Whistling Monster by Jamila Gavin. Walker Books 2009
p.52-53: 'A Crow And A Scarecrow' from New And Collected Poems For Children by Carol Ann Duffy. Published by Faber & Faber, 2019.
Copyright © Carol Ann Duffy. Reproduced by permission of the author c/o Rogers, Coleridge & White Ltd., 20 Powis Mews, London W11 1JN

Pages 3 and 64 contain public sector information licensed under the Open Government Licence v3.0. http://www.nationalarchives.gov.uk/doc/open-government-licence/version/3/

Images & Clipart throughout the book from Corel ® and Clipart.com

National Curriculum Content Areas

Use the table below to record how pupils are doing in each of the National Curriculum Content Areas.

		2a Word Meaning	2b Retrieval	2c Summarising	2d Inference	2e Prediction	2f Text Meaning	2g Language	2h Comparison
Text 1: Daffodils	Set 1	Q4	Q1 Q2	Q6	Q5			Q3	
	Set 2	Q3		Q5	Q2b Ch		Q2a	Q1	Q4
Text 2: Winter Paralympics	Set 1		Q2 Q3 Q4	Q1			Q6		Q5
	Set 2	Q2	Q4		Q3 Ch			Q1 Q5	
Text 3: Conker	Set 1	Q6	Q1 Q2 Q3 Q4	Q5					
	Set 2				Q1 Q4b Ch	Q4a	Q3 Q5	Q2	
Text 4: The Coming of Raven	Set 1	Q2 Q6	Q1 Q3 Q4	Q5					
	Set 2		Q1		Q3a Q3b Ch			Q2 Q5	Q4
Text 5: Helicopters	Set 1	Q1	Q2a Q2b Q3 Q4 Q5	Q6					
	Set 2	Q5			Ch		Q1	Q3 Q4	Q2
Text 6: It's Today	Set 1	Q3	Q2 Q5		Q1		Q4	Q6a Q6b	
	Set 2	Q2c			Q1 Q2a Q3 Q4 Ch			Q5	Q2b
Text 7: The Sealed Room	Set 1	Q5	Q1 Q2	Q3 Q6					Q4
	Set 2		Q3	Q4a	Q1 Q2 Q5		Q4b Ch		
Text 8: Fairtrade Bananas	Set 1	Q4	Q1 Q2 Q5	Q3				Q6	
	Set 2	Q5			Q1 Q3 Ch		Q2a Q2b	Q4	
Text 9: The Crow and the Scarecrow	Set 1	Q5	Q1 Q3	Q4			Q2		Q6
	Set 2				Q1 Q4 Q5 Ch			Q2 Q3 Q6	
Total									